# FOREWORD

I'm not sure this sort of book really needs an introduction, – there's not much to explain, nothing complicated about it, – simply a collection of cartoons and a few little verses, – purely to entertain.

The drawings are from the farming scene, and generally involve a peasant character called 'Sep', who has emerged, almost by accident, from various writings and cartoons over the past few years.

I reckon there's a bit of Sep in every working farmer, whether he's been left half the parish by his benevolent grannie and grows four tons of barley to the acre, – or is a hard-up tenant with just a hundred geriatric blackie yowes.

Anybody who has survived a lambing, pleaded with a bank manager, nearly murdered a persistent worm-drench rep, been kicked in the Y-fronts by a suckler calf, watched the heavens open onto a field of hay ready to bale, viewed the hunt gallop over his winter wheat, and choked on a tax demand, – will recognise Sep.

Anybody who's had a brainless, over-enthusiastic collie dog, a knackered combine on a fine August afternoon, a burst water pipe on Christmas morning, a visit from the safety inspector just as little Willie falls into the dipper, or a busload of townies pass by as you're beating an awkward auld yow t' death with a net stake, – will recognise Sep (or themselves).

Wives who've put up with the highs and lows of farming husbands will recognise the foul temper, the chauvinist attitude, the Midas touch and the revolting wellie socks.

They may never quite understand how that canny, weather-beaten old 'pussy-cat' asleep on the chair with his mouth and his flies half open, can turn (like a Jekyll and Hyde), into a raging maniac who kicks tractors that don't start, or wufflers that decline to wuffle.

They'll never quite _____ Sep (or whoever), can men_____ of hairy pot-bellied cattl_____ go to pieces at the prosp_____

Townies generally _____ which is often early ninetee_____ the subtle blend of afters_____arty, which proves to be _____bjects sticking out from the bottom of his sleeves.

Sep then is the universal peasant, who constantly complains that his job is impossible, but wouldn't (and couldn't) swop with anybody.

The occasional verses that punctuate this book are taken from a collection called 'the upteen faces of farming', characters who are an integral part of country life – the auctioneer, the vet, the shepherd and so on. These, and some of the cartoons, have appeared in NFU magazines and *Livestock Farming* – 'hope you enjoy them.

*Hartburn, 1983*                    HENRY BREWIS

*First published 1983*
*Reprinted eight times 1983-2004*

*Illustrations and text copyright © Henry Brewis, 1983.*

*ISBN 1-903366-70-4*

Published by: Old Pond Publishing Dencora Business Centre, 36 White House Road, Ipswich, IP1 5LT United Kingdom

www.oldpond.com

Printed and bound in Finland by WS Bookwell

**SPRING . . . when fancies lightly turn . . .**

'C'mon out m' darlin's, – it's Spring, – honest . . . !'

'Now girls, – it'll soon be lambing time again, and we'll have to decide who's to have the privilege of suddenly dropping dead for no apparent reason . . .'

'. . . what do y' mean, – we'll maybe get married if y' have a good lambin' . . . ?'

henry brewis.

'. . . and don't look so bloody clever, – y' haven't even lambed yet, have y' . . . ?'

## 'THE SHEPHERD'

'A peculiar breed is the shepherd
tending his flock to the end
you might think that he's wise when you look in
   his eyes
but in fact he's away round the bend
if he could he would tell you he's crackers
but the truth is he'd break down and weep
he just lives for the day when the tup's put away
and an evening spent paring sheep's feet
he only believes what he wants to believe
nowt that he rears ever dies
and a night at the pub is no bloody good
if he cannot just sit tellin' lies
two hundred and ten per cent lambin' this year
the best yowes for many a mile
clipped three hundred and three just before tea
(and without so much as a smile)
there's just one who could tell y' the truth of
   course
how he strangled that champion mule hogg
how the tup met its fate when the lambin' was late
and who shot that good collie dog
aye his wife knows there's really no prospects
with a fella devoted to sheep
he'll rant and he'll rave from now to the grave
and shout git away bye in his sleep . . .'

'. . . why don't y' go home missus, – you're obviously quite familiar with this particular miracle of nature . . .'

'. . . is this an Olympic event, Dad . . . ?'

'. . . happens every Spring, – comes out stoned on a glass of Cyprus sherry and his overdraft doubled . . .'

'. . . just a little bit further, Son, – then I'll show y' how to persuade the ewe t' take the other lamb . . .'

'. . . watch your language Sep, – he's from the Bank, says he's concerned about his investment . . .'

# 'THE ACCOUNTANT'

'He sits at his desk with his horn-rimmed specs
doing sums on a calculator
and come rain or shine you know bloody fine
there's a bill to pay sooner or later
he adds and subtracts and works out your tax
messing about with the figures
you've done fairly well so how in the hell
is that overdraft still gettin' bigger
those accounts are too much it's all double dutch
so you 'phone up for him to explain
but his cute office bird says haven't you heard
he's away to his villa in Spain . . .'

'. . . that proves it, – yer father *was* a bloody labrador . . . !'

'. . . when I was his age, I'd done a day's work by now . . . !'

'. . . aaah, look Sep, – the first real sign of Spring . . .'

'. . . quick as y' can Vicar, – we've got a yow lambin' . . .'

'. . . ah Mister Thompson, – there you are . . .'

## 'THE REP'

'He's from Fluko International
and his patter's well rehearsed
but he comes when things are dying
and the water pipe is burst
he's bright he's keen and eager
with a spotless company car
and he's here to tell y' kindly
how incompetent you are
he's an expert he's a genius
and he comes with words of warning, –
he's the seventh bloody worm-drench rep
you've had since Monday morning . . . !'

'. . . before that Selina Scott came on in the mornin's, y' were half-way round the farm by now . . .'

'. . . and where we come from we've abolished nuclear weapons, racial prejudice and sheep!'

'... every year about this time somebody forecasts a record harvest and a record lambin', – how come we're not all bloody millionaires Charlie ... ?'

'... verily thou hast rejoiced enough over the one that was lost, – now for God's sake let us get back with the
other ninety-nine ...'

'. . . we're just playin' vets Mother, – Willie's going t' give Dad a copper injection, then we'll worm 'im . . .'

## 'THE VET'

'She got a tin of Terramycin
and a bottleful of dope
a pint of penicillin
and a canny bit of hope
the vet was optimistic
he'd worked miracles before
but the yow was quite determined
and she died at half past four
the vet was very sad indeed
he thought it might've lived
and I was disappointed too
'cos he charged me thirty quid . . .'

'I'd appreciate it if you didn't fill it in 'til *after* the lambin' . . .'

'. . . what do y' think Willie, – is it yoga, or have the sheep finally beaten 'im . . . ?'

'. . . what's the matter Woman, – have y' never seen anybody set on a lamb before . . . ?'

'. . . C'mon then, – what's all this we hear about a 45 per cent rise in farm incomes . . . ?'

'. . . I cannot sell 'er at that price Tommy, – she's m' favourite . . . !'

'. . . I think he's tidying up the garden today . . .'

'. . . right lads, – y've got ten seconds before I slip 'er into gear, – one . . . two . . .'

'He has a 1.3 Allegro
and a bed of champion leeks
gets paid for havin' holidays
drinks umpteen pints a week
spends a fortune on the gee-gees
and never sheds a tear
but tatties milk 'n beef 'n bread
are always far too dear
his wife works at the Co-op
plays bingo each weekend

they have 2.7 children
and a semi in Wallsend
they come crawling out on Sundays
park at nature's green back door
play football in your hayfield
with a car-load from Tow Law
they meander through the byeways
pickin' brambles down the lane
and if you lived where they live mate
you'd do the bloody same . . . !'

'. . . this is no time t' be collectin' for the RSPCA, Vicar . . . !'

'. . . we'll have a proper holiday this year he says, – just you 'n me he says, – second ruddy honeymoon he says, – away from it all, he says . . . !'

'. . . he could be wrong dear, the forecast isn't *always* right, y' know . . .'

'. . . some day comrades, all this will be ours!'

'. . . 'can't stop now Sarge, – the forecast says it'll rain before dark . . . !'

## 'THE VILLAGE BOBBY'

'Eight foot high and fifteen stone
dark blue suit and size twelve feet
big black bike and telephone
and time to keep his garden neat
just look in at leek club dance
never know what he might hear
give that drunk another chance
that youth a clip along the ear
who pinched the apples from the hall
who gaffed a salmon Tuesday night
the likely lads he knew them all
and they knew he could bark and bite
he was common sense and law
not nine t' five plus overtime
tatties left at his back door
I'll scratch your back you scratch mine, –
they sold his house took him away
bought him a big flash Ford
now he sits along the motorway
with a plastic bag unloved and bored . . .'

'. . . not now Sweep . . . !'

'. . . how do y' know mother's got mildew, – she's just got here . . . !'

'. . . I don't suppose y' brought the *Farmers Weekly* with y' . . .'

'. . . never mind Son, – Rome wasn't built in a day y' know . . .'

'. . . lucky, eh? – just got it under cover before the rain . . .'

'. . . any place wi' that many sheep is bound t' be a problem . . . !'

'. . . d' y' fancy tryin' your kiss of life trick again, Charlie . . . ?'

## 'THE CLIPPER'

'The first one had no rise at all
sticky tight and full of grease
backbone like a railway line
kicked and wriggled all the time
couldn't wrap the fleece
picked a belly bare and smooth
a gimmer young and fit
clippers hummin' like a song
no sooner started she was gone
minus half a tit
horny mule easy caught
like handles on a jug
stupid bitch was seven crop
I thought the blood would never stop
cut off her near-side lug
got a nervous twitchin' thing
who jumped about wild-eyed
she left me sittin' on the floor
trousers ripped and then what's more
she lay quite still and died . . . !'

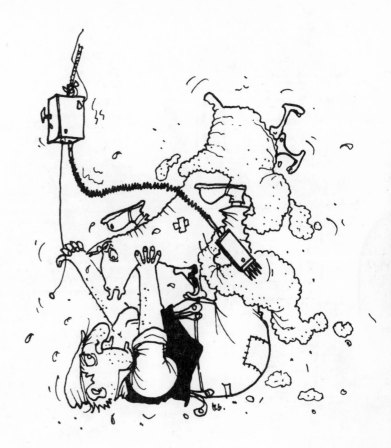

'. . . that's it then, – put the receiver in, – we pay off 3p in the pound and I buy the yowes back for nowt . . . !'

'. . . I still say Sweep will *not* appreciate Benidorm . . .'

'. . . c'mon girls, it's luvly, – really . . .'

'. . . what ever happened to that bloke who used t' rabbit on about feather-bed farmers, – remember him lads . . . ?'

'. . . yes, t'night Sep, – *this* is *your* life . . . !'

# 'THE EXPERT'

'You see 'im on the telly
in the papers every week
he's on every new committee
and his wellies never leak
he dresses well he's always clean
impressive on the phone
at least when you can catch 'im
'cos he's seldom found at home

he can talk about gross margins
understands the EEC
all his acres are in hectares
and he's got a good degree
the green pound holds no mysteries
but can he tell us why
in spite of being brilliant
he's as broke as you and I . . .'

'. . . I just asked him for some luck money, that's all . . . !'

'. . . it's the boss, Doctor, – lost 'is temper with the baler again . . .'

'. . . what y' mean, she's mad-a-bullin', – get the damn thing off m' Cadillac!'

'. . . some mornin's, Willie, – I get the feelin' that you 'n me are the only fellas workin' in the whole world . . .'

## 'THE A.I. MAN'

'He's got Blonde Aquitaine
a good Hereford strain
and a Charolais off the top shelf
and if she's in season
he'll service your Friesian
and do the job all by himself
with his armful of sires
he wanders round byres
seducing old girls on the way
but I bet they're surprised
when he looks in their eyes
and claims he's the bull of the day . . . !'

'. . . got 'im on a job creation scheme, – I think he's been one of them SAS blokes . . . !'

'. . . oh God it's him again, – he'll try anything to get a bit of sympathy . . .'

'. . . it's the same every year, – they try to buy the goat, – then ask for five million pesetas luck money . . .'

'. . . this must be another one y' clipped last year, Charlie, – its lugs are missin' . . .'

'. . . hold it Willie, hold it, – I think we've gotta wild oat problem here . . .'

## 'THE CONSERVATIONIST'

'He plodges through the clarty holes
he wanders through the trees
he burrows in the hedgerows
for spuggies mice and fleas
in amongst the long grass
with the spiders and the bugs
the poor bewildered beetles
and nasty slimy slugs
he's mother nature's favourite son
a friend of frogs and toads
and dead unlucky hedgehogs
squashed on busy country roads
he's the saviour of the flora
and the fauna everywhere
especially if it's threatened
especially if it's rare
the protector of the universe
the only one who cares
for the lesser spotted lapwings
foxes moths and hares
the only one to save them
from man's eternal greed
but does he know the difference
twixt a flower and a weed
does he know the difference
can he pass the primary test
of who's a welcome visitor
and who's a bloody pest
will he leave old mother nature
to sort out all the pieces
or will he not be happy 'til
we're all endangered species . . . ?'

'. . . we've got to stop her, Gladys, – I need her t' bale straw tomorrow . . . !'

'. . . sorry mate, but y' know what the rules are, – y' gotter stay in a full minute . . .'

'. . . wrong bloody farm, Son, – you're supposed t' be sprayin' Charlie's barley, – not my mule yowes . . .'

'. . . the man from the Mutual's here t' see you, – it's about your personal accident policy . . .'

'. . . alright then, – who sold the combine t' the scrap man for 25p and a Mars bar . . . ?'

'. . . well, that's the last time *she'll* creep in here and eat m' show leeks . . . !'

'He said this auger isn't guarded
as it took his finger off
he said this floorboard's nearly rotten
as he fell into the trough
he said these granary steps are dangerous
as the second one gave way

and when he slipped into the dipper
I knew it wasn't quite his day
he said that bull could do some damage
as it hit him like a train, –
and we had to get an ambulance
to take him home again . . .'

'. . . Dad, – teddy wants to know what's wrong with the combine . . .'

'. . . well you'd be huffed as well, if y' thought *that's* all y' were worth . . . !'

'. . . right, Pet, – where's this fancy washin' machine I promised t' mend . . . ?'

'... Sep, you know perfectly well the regulations do not include my mother ...!'

'. . . he's the only bloke round here who understands the green pound . . .'

79

'. . . put a couple of whiskies in his coffee, and he'll certify anything . . . !'

'Three cheers for the Ministry Grader
he's a charming and lovable bloke
so get down on your knees
say thank you and please
and remember to laugh at his jokes

hats off to the Mart Ayatollah
always be humble and meek
he's knocked three kilos off
but the man's still a toff
he could nicely reject them next week . . . !'

'. . . no, not me Tommy, – I didn't bid . . .'

'. . . he's after Willie, – 'cos Willie started the combine up, and Dad was inside it . . . !'

'. . . y' *knew* he was comin', – didn't y' . . . ?'

'. . . did somebody say the recession was over . . . ?'

'. . . I get the feelin' he expected a wee bit more than this, Gentlemen . . .'

'A peculiar bird is the auctioneer
leaping about in his nest
nothing he sells is ever too dear
and certainly bred from the best

stand on y' will that beast's for nowt
(it'll still cost y' five hundred quid)
yer in yer out he points he shouts, –
and y've got it with maybe the only bid . . . !'

'. . . alright, alright, – so we *won't* be going to the harvest festival t'night . . .'

'. . . does this 'n belong t' the wife Sep . . . ?'

'. . . Charlie, I don't think you're concentratin', – your mind's not on the job is it . . . ?'

`. . . I say, Nigel, – do you imagine they counted you and I in the latest unemployment figures . . . ?'

## 'THE LANDLORD'

'Have a thought for your destitute landlord
doff your cap and push back the tears
as he sits on his throne in his cold stately home
adjusting your rent each three years
do y' think he enjoys shootin' pheasants
chasin' foxes from each nook 'n cranny
just forget that old dream of how life might've
    been
if his grandad had married your granny . . .'

'. . . for God's sake be nice to him Freda, – 'til I get the car hitched on . . . !'

'. . . he says these sheep are from very high ground, and they'll thrive anywhere . . . !'

'. . . don't be ridiculous, Sep, – they don't *need* a pulpy kidney injection . . .'

'. . . she reckons there's a ton and a half on the bathroom floor like this, – what's it worth?'

'. . . Sep, – come and remove this thing from Mother's room at once . . . !'

'. . . what y' mean, you're an "innocent gimmer", – you were four crop *last* year . . . !'

'. . . we're from the Water Authority, – we understand you are somewhat reluctant to pay your latest account . . .'

## 'THE COUNCIL MAN'

'Auld Albert had a length all his
down through the village up the hill
from Charlie Thompson's farm lane end
right t' the burn at Mitford Mill
he trimmed the verges cleaned the ditch
and scythed the docks and nettles low
brushed all the gravel into heaps
and kept his stretch of road just so
all summer autumn winter spring
he hardly missed a single day
through sunshine frost and falling leaves
and all on agricultural pay
but Albert's gone redundant now
they said they couldn't meet the bill
and gone the tidy length he kept
down through the village up the hill
instead the yellow army rolls
in yellow trucks and yellow vans
drinks yellow tea in yellow huts
all glazy leggin'd to a man
now all the docks grow ten feet high
the ditch is full to overflow
they grit the banks on double time
and take their turns at Stop 'n Go
and yet with all their fancy gear
with rates at umpteen thousand quid
down through the village up the hill
seems they can't do what Albert did . . .'

101

'. . . Sep, I think it's time you put your sheep inside during the Winter . . .'

'. . . don't tell me, – there's a dozen final demands, eighteen free offers, somethin' from the Inland Revenue, and six Christmas cards from relations we forgot about . . .'

'No, I'm afraid y've just missed 'im . . .'

'C'mon y' miserable old thing, – we haven't spent *half* a friesian bullock yet . . . !'

'. . . I think it's the three wise men . . .'

'. . . and may the blessings of a bountiful and joyous New Year be with you too, Reverend . . . !'

## 'THE VICAR'

'The Reverend Arthur Crumbling views his Mondays
    with a smile
he can potter round the vicarage or stroll a
    country mile
there's a christening here on Tuesday but it's not 'til
    half past three
and the doting little mother will invite him back
    for tea
on Wednesday a funeral all dressed up in
    Sunday clothes
ah well you bury some y' christen some that's the way
    it goes
nowt to do on Thursday but the bishop may call in
might ask him for a rise I think when he's on his
    second gin
Friday might go fishing give the sermon text some
    thought
how 'bout "blessed is the poacher, provided he's not
    caught"
a wedding on the Saturday the Thompson's daughter
    June
and judging by the size of her not a day too soon
then ye gods it's Sunday work the live-long day
singin' hymns and preachin' brethren let us pray
let us pray for Monday when the living has some style
and I can potter round the vicarage or stroll a country
    mile . . .'

109

'. . . stand back, – you're just in time t' see this useless creature exported t' France . . . !'

'. . . what y' makin' all the fuss about, – didn't I *promise* to take y' Christmas shopping . . . ?'

'. . . all I said was, – why not try countin' sheep. . . .'

'. . . bought another combine, Charlie, couldn't refuse the offer, – they knocked a thousand quid off, gave me a
Mini Metro, – and threw Gloria in for luck . . .'

'. . . did y' always want to be a farmer, Dad . . . ?'

## 'THE HILL FARMER'

'Spare a thought for the man from oot bye
with his cap and his dog and his stick
through the sleet and the rain does he ever
    complain
if he didn't y'd think he was sick, –
spare a thought for the man from the hill
where it's winter while spring at the coast
say a prayer for his cows and his poor blackie
    yowes
and his subsidy cheque in the post . . .'

'. . . happens every January, Doctor, he just goes t' pieces, – sits there and stares at that envelope, refuses t' open it . . .'

'. . . I wonder if Princess Anne realises that Mark could end up lookin' like you after thirty years of farmin' . . . ?'

'. . . come bye . . . !!!'

'I told y' didn't I, – I *said* y' wouldn't get a lie-in on Christmas mornin' . . .'

'. . . how many times have I told y', – for God's sake don't feed them 'til I've got a clear run to the gate . . . !'

'. . . says he's stoppin' in there 'til it's all over . . .'

## 'THE POSTIE'

'Postie where do you get it from
your van must overflow
all these firms that send me stuff
I want no more I've had enough
isn't there somewhere else to go?
a leaflet here on worms in sheep
and yet another magazine
(on pigs this time) they're two a penny
at least I never pay for any, –
and the biggest bloody phone bill ever seen
here's a catalogue that weighs a ton
filled with things that I don't need
a competition with a chance
to win a holiday in France
and more advice on barley seed
a little card from ICI
says Nitram's cheap this year
and an invite to a seminar
seventh one this week so far
with coffee sandwiches and beer
eight more fertiliser ads today
and a bill I thought I'd paid
American Express still trying hard
to give away their credit card
provided that I tell them what I've made
what a load of rubbish comes
floating tumbling through the door
from companies who surely see
they'll never make a sale with me
but still they try for more
into the fire most of it goes
'cept the statement from the bank
the letter from a long-lost mate
the tax demand that cannot wait
and a cheque received with thanks
postie where do you get it from
your van must be too small
but I suppose I've got to say
it would be a duller day
if you never called at all . . .'

123

'. . . and where are all the factory farming demonstrators this morning I wonder . . . ?'

'. . . is it *next* Sunday you're gonna tell 'im what to do with his auld yowes Willie . . . ?'

'. . . you'll never believe it, Pet, – but we won . . . !'

'. . . t' tell you the truth Tommy, I want rid of them, – we'll take the first genuine bid y' get . . .'

'. . . there, I told you it was Dad, – Santa Claus never used words like that . . . !'